ABC
is for
CHRISTMAS

by Jane Werner Watson

illustrated by Sally Augustiny

gb

GOLDEN PRESS

Western Publishing Company, In

Racine, Wisconsin

© 1974 by Western Publishing Company

Third Printing, 1977

D1445089

Aa

A is for angel.

Bb

B is for bell.

Cc

C is for candle and carol, as well.

Dd

D is for donkey.

Ee

E is for elf

F is for fun, filling Christmas itself.

G is for gifts we give.

H h

H is for holly.

I i

I is for ice cream, and

J j

J is for jolly.

Kk

K is for kings who came.

Ll

L is for lamb.

M is for Mary
and manger and Man.

Mm

Nn

N is for Noel.

Oo

Offering is O.

Pp

P is for presents

and playthings, also.

Q is for quiet times.

Rr

R is for rose.

Ss

S is for Santa Claus, sleigh bells—

and snows.

Tt

T is for tree trimmings.

U is for us.

Uu

V is for village and visits by bus.

W is wise men
and winter and white.

Ww

Xx

X is a letter,
the sign of the Christ.

Y is for yule logs
that crackle and glow.

Yy

Zz

Z is for zither—
for carols, you know.

We could start over, again and again,
For Christmas has meanings without any end.